razor LOOKS

Sí Salon Publishing Ltd

7 East Lodge, Inner Park Road, London SW19 6DE, England

Tel. +44 20 8785 2863   Fax +44 20 8785 0199

Devised & Produced by Simon Webb

Art Direction by Michael Breese

Reproduction and Print by Centro Grafico Ambrosiano, Milan, Italy

razor LOOKS

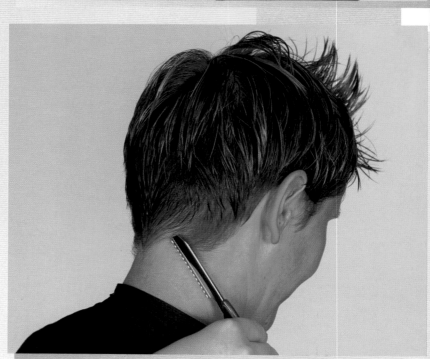

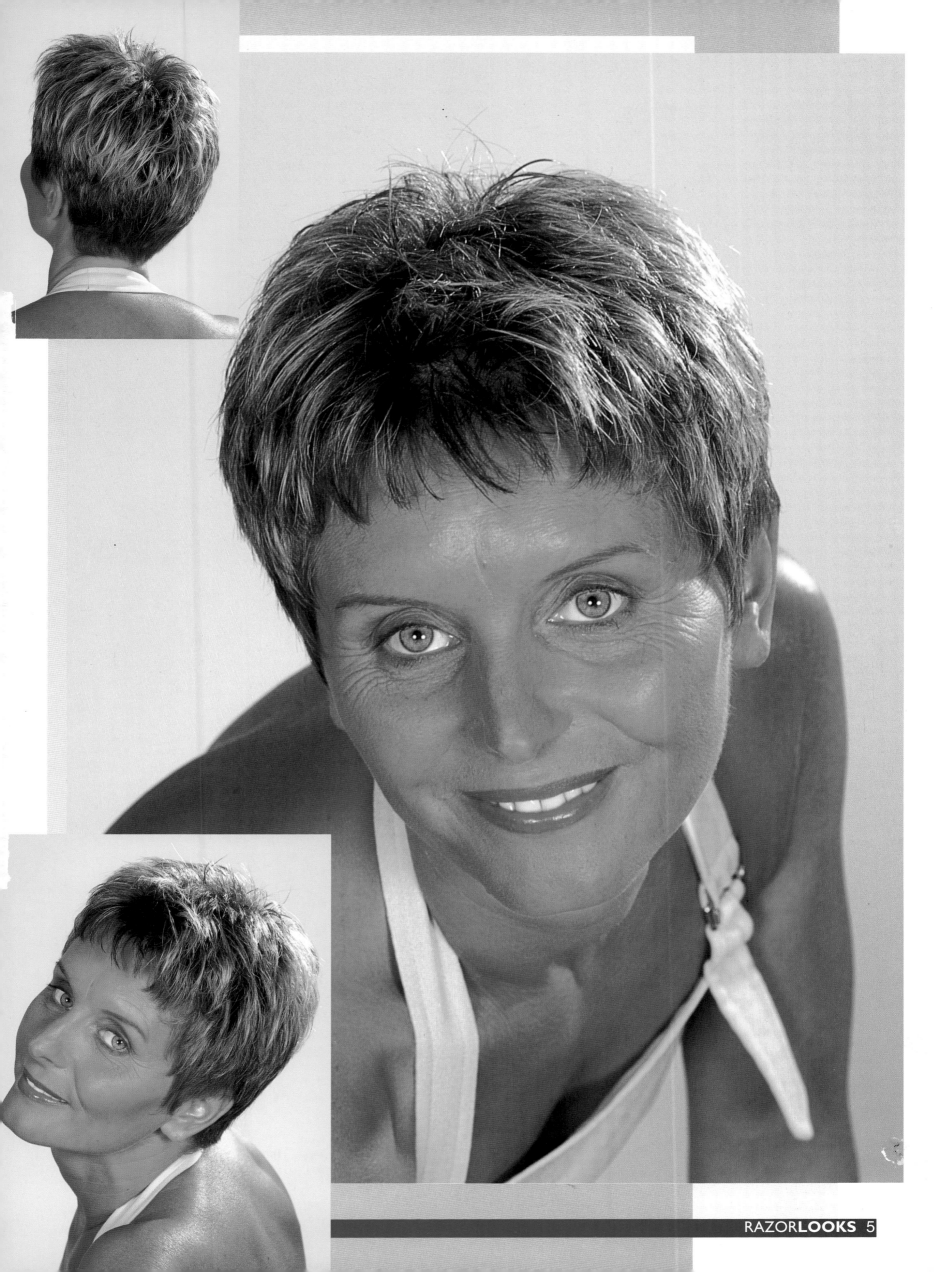

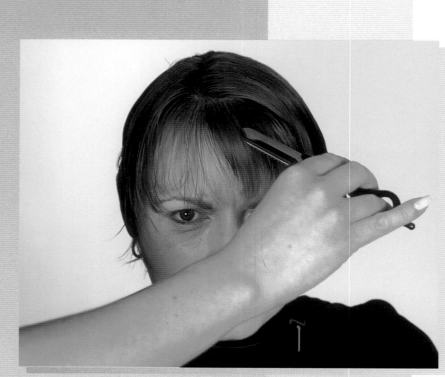

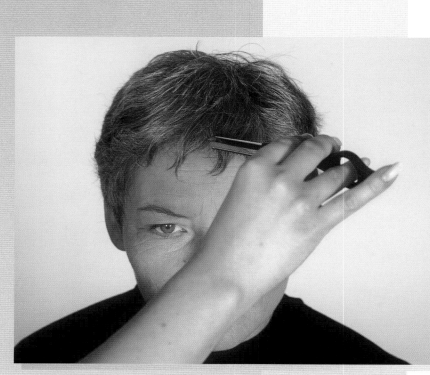

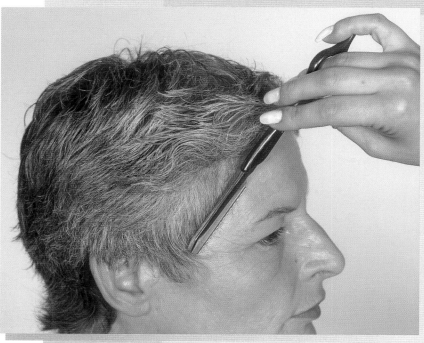

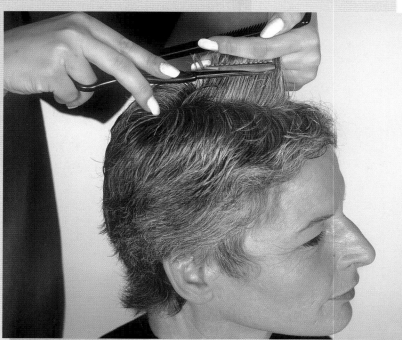

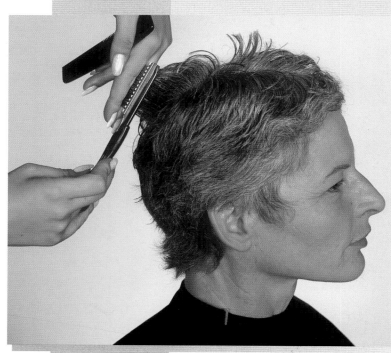

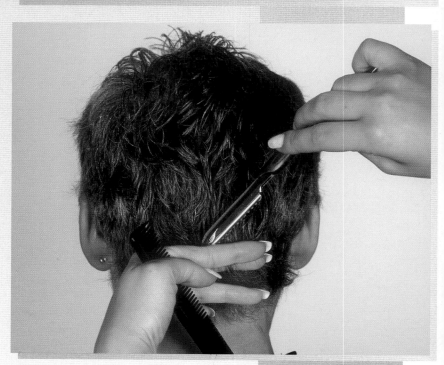

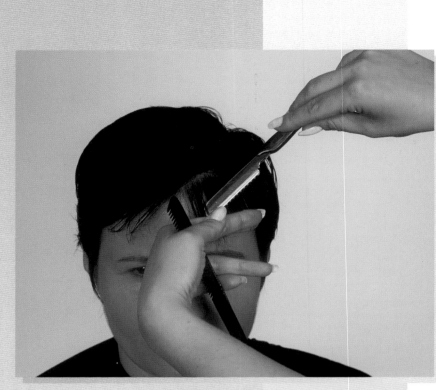

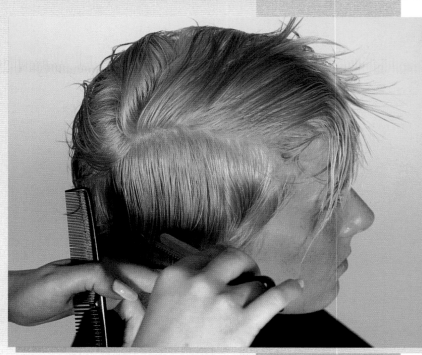

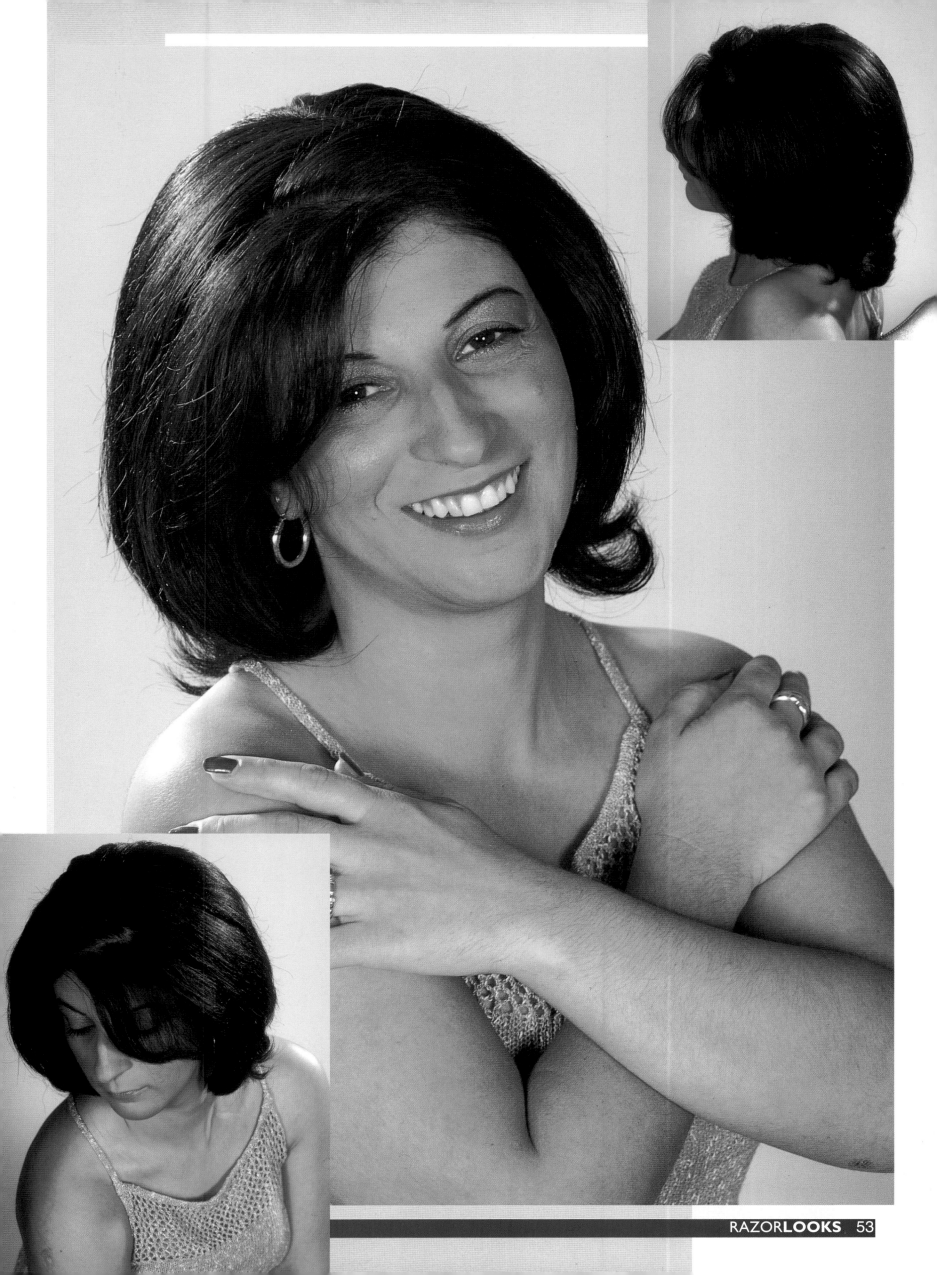

Nora Zamora / Philip Pelusi USA

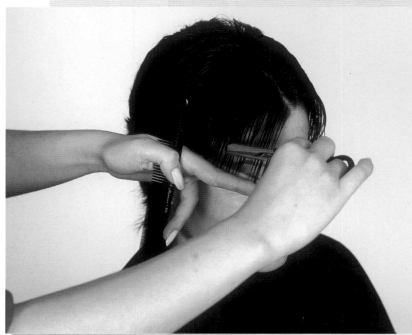

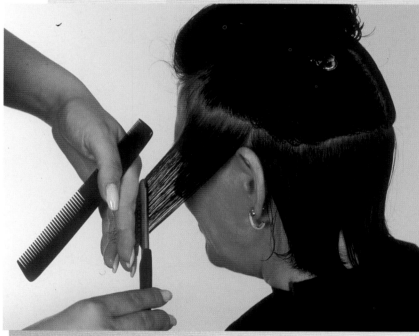

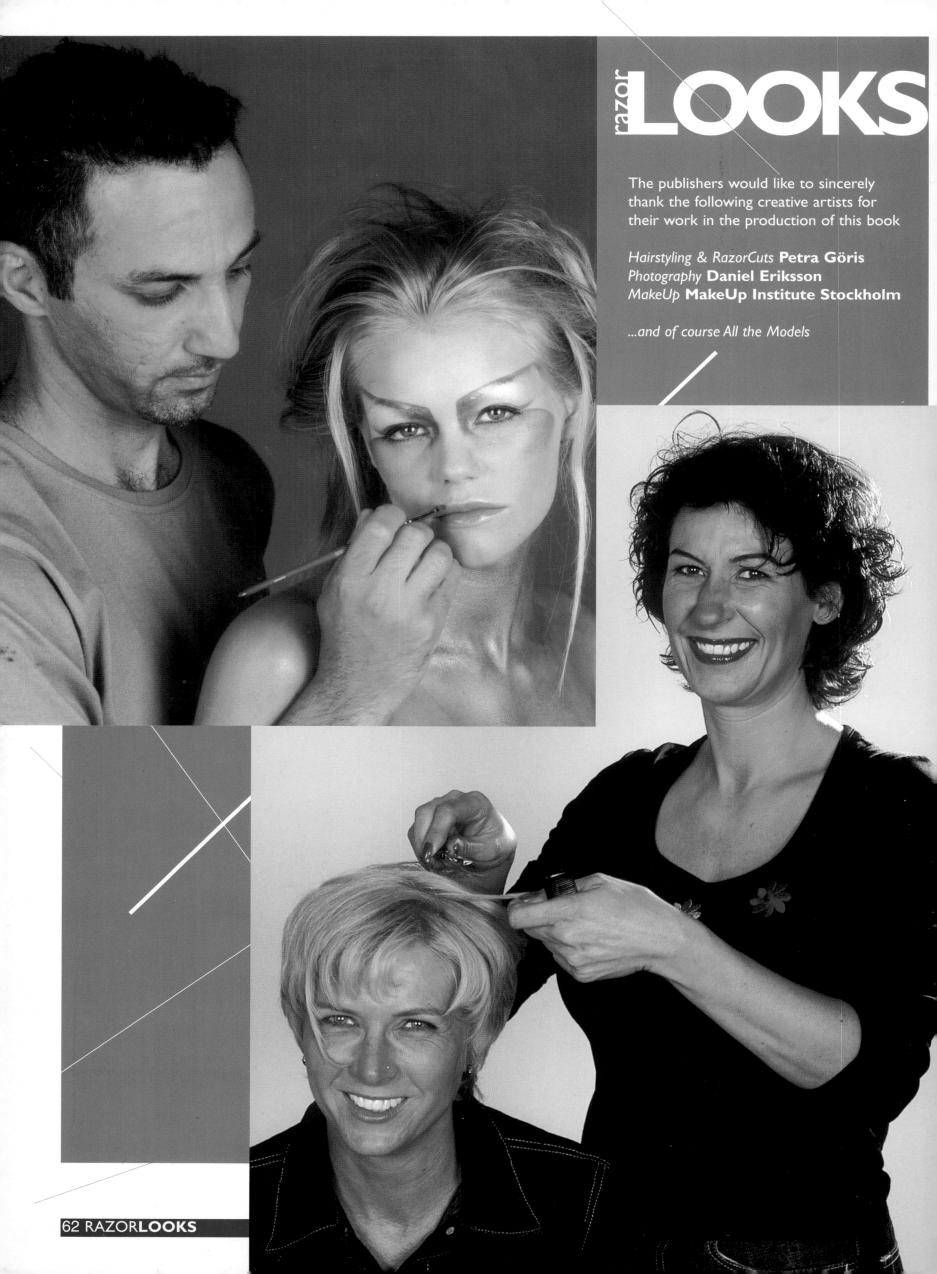

razorLOOKS

The publishers would like to sincerely thank the following creative artists for their work in the production of this book

Hairstyling & RazorCuts **Petra Göris**
Photography **Daniel Eriksson**
MakeUp **MakeUp Institute Stockholm**

...and of course All the Models

Make-UpArtist
EDUCATION
Film TV Theater Commercials Fashion

Stockholms Make-up Institute is widele recognised as the international school for the make-up profession. Hairdressers and students converge on Swedens capital to benefit from a full 16 week intensive education, whilst enjoying the rich and artistically inspiring culture Stockholm has become so famous for. Why not take the next step on a road to a glamourous and exciting future?

MAKE UP
INSTITUTE
STOCKHOLM

For more information please contact us on: Tel. +46 (0)8 30 06 40 Fax +46 (0)8 30 06 45

Make Up Institute Stocholm Frejgatan 73 113 26 Stockholm Sweden www.makeupinstitute.com

FEATHER
- J A P A N -

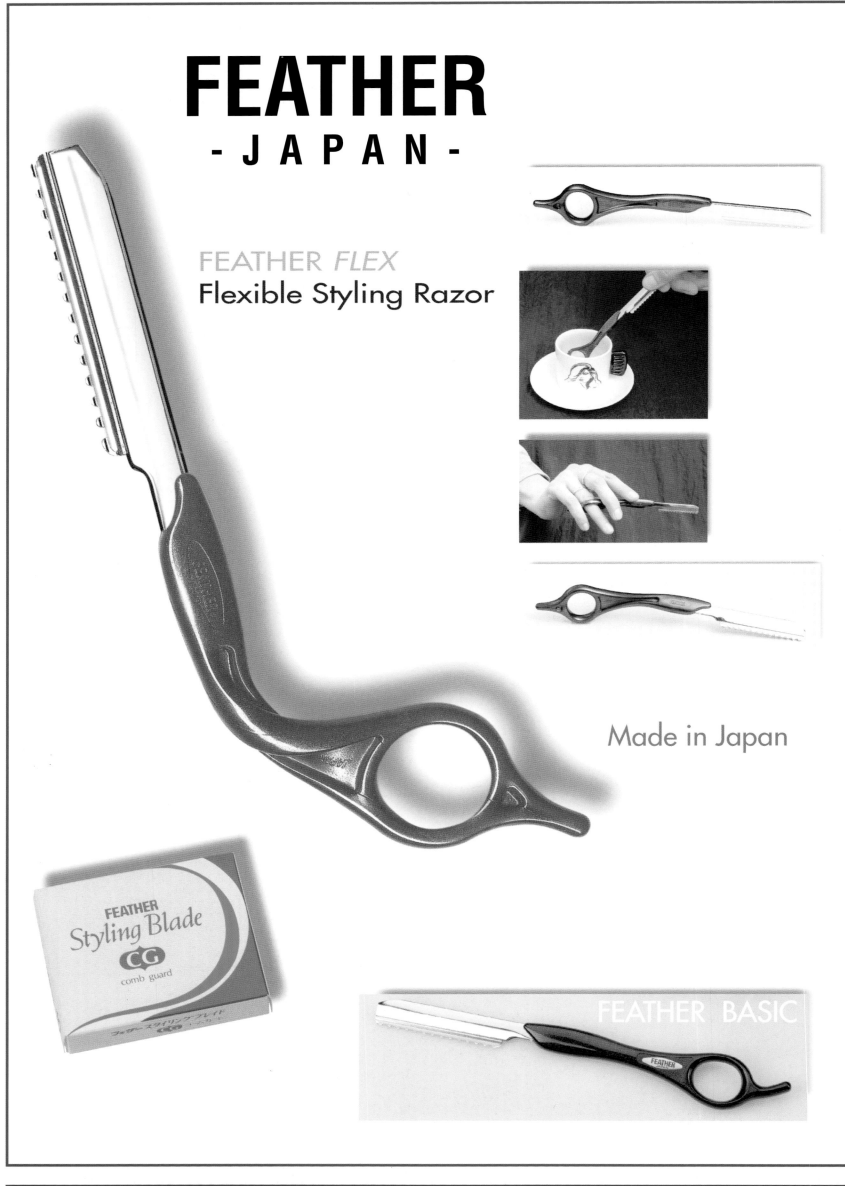

FEATHER *FLEX*
Flexible Styling Razor

Made in Japan

FEATHER
Styling Blade
CG
comb guard

FEATHER BASIC

razor LOOKS

83012

EXCLUSIVE DISTRIBUTION

Germany, Austria, Switzerland, Netherlands, Turkey & Mauritius
Trend-Design GmbH
Brüderstr. 16 · Postfach 2305
D-32052 Herford
Tel. 05221 / 54900
Fax 05221 / 56890
e-mail: trend-design-gmbh@t-online.de

Trend-Design GMBH

Denmark, Sweden, Norway & Finland
HAARO Friseurbedarf
Mangenberger Str. 88
42655 Solingen
Tel. (02 12) 20 93 90
Fax (02 12) 20 86 43

HAARO
Friseurbedarf
Handelsgesellschaft mbH

Greece & Cyprus
VANGELIS SVENTZO
23, Milon Str.
Area code: 104-44
Kolonos-Athens
Tel. (01) 5150618
Fax (01) 5121277

Belgium & Luxembo
SFEO-ART bvba
Verbindingsstraat 10
2288 Bouwel - Grobb
Tel./Fax 014 / 50 15 2

Australia & New Zeal
Western Imports Pty. L
21 Mary Parade
Rydalmere
NSW 2116
Tel: (02) 9898 0299
Fax (02) 9898 0283

U.S.A.
On Point, Inc.
235 West Second
Madrid, IA 50156
Tel. 1.800.356.1586
Fax 1.515.795.2434

On Point ELIT
U.S.A. PUBLISH

Korea
BEAUTY WORLD NEWS CO. LTD
98-28 Hwa-Gok-Bon-Dong
Kang So-Gu
Seoul
Tel. 2-779-6111
Fax 2-779-6113

Israel, Jordan & Egypt
OKK Marketing & Image Ltd.

CERU PROJECT INTERNATIONAL

O.K.K.
MARKETING & IMAGE LTD.